Mail today ...
and good behavior
will be on its way!

If card is missing, write to:
Help Me Be Good
c/o Scholastic
P.O. Box 6038
Jefferson City, MO 65102-6038

Well-behaved kids start with these FREE GIFTS!

FREE CDs!

FREE Parents Guide

FREE Reading Guide

FREE TRIAL!

FREE BOOK!

card is missing, ite to:

Help Me Be Good
c/o Scholastic
P.O. Box 6038
Jefferson City, MO
65102-6038

Help Me Be Good! Instead of saying "no-no"... say "YES" to good behavior!

CODE: 964803WVA-3

☐ **YES!** Please send my FREE BOOK, *Disobeying*, FREE BONUS GIFTS, the Sing-Along CDs, Parent's Guide, and "Reading Together is Fun" Guide, plus two more Help Me Be Good books, *Being Selfish* and *Teasing*, for my seven-day free preview.

If not delighted with my trial books, I'll return them at your expense and owe nothing. On the other hand, if they help my child understand the "do's" and "don'ts" of *Teasing* and *Being Selfish*, I'll pay just $5.48 per book, plus shipping and handling on the entire shipment, and become a member of the program.

Then, about four weeks later I'll receive two more books in the series. If I keep *Whining* and *Tattling*, I'll pay only $5.48 for each, plus shipping and handling.

About four weeks after that, I'll receive the remaining 24 books in a single shipment. This gives my child the complete series to read and enjoy, while I pay for only one book per month at $5.48 each, plus shipping and handling.

I may examine the books for seven days and return any I don't want at your expense. My FREE BOOK, *Disobeying*, FREE Sing-Along CDs, Parent's Guide and "Reading Together is Fun" Guide are mine to keep even if I purchase nothing.

Print Child's Full Name: _____ Birthdate: _____ ☐ Boy ☐ Girl

Month/Day/Year

Print Your Full Name ☐ Mr. ☐ Mrs. ☐ Ms. _____

Address _____ Apt. _____

City _____ State _____ Zip _____

Telephone (_____) _____

E-mail (to confirm your order) _____

Have you bought anything by mail in the last: ☐ 6 months ☐ Year ☐ Never   Do you own a computer? ☐ Yes ☐ No

Sales tax where applicable. Late charges apply to overdue payments. All orders subject to approval. Out-of-stock titles may be replaced by alternate selections.

DETACH HERE AND MAIL TODAY!   Art © 1988 Living Skills Press   TM & © Scholastic Inc.

Mail today ...
and good behavior
will be on its way!

If card is missing, write to:
Help Me Be Good
c/o Scholastic
P.O. Box 6038
Jefferson City, MO 65102-6038

Well-behaved kids start with these FREE GIFTS!

FREE CDs!

FREE Parents Guide

FREE Reading Guide

FREE BOOK!

FREE TRIAL!

...card is missing, write to:

Help Me Be Good
c/o Scholastic
P.O. Box 6038
Jefferson City, MO
65102-6038

Help Me Be Good! Instead of saying "no-no"... say "YES" to good behavior!

CODE: 964803WVA-3

☐ **YES!** Please send my FREE BOOK, *Disobeying*, FREE BONUS GIFTS, the Sing-Along CDs, Parent's Guide, and "Reading Together is Fun" Guide, plus two more Help Me Be Good books, *Being Selfish* and *Teasing*, for my seven-day free preview.

If not delighted with my trial books, I'll return them at your expense and owe nothing. On the other hand, if they help my child understand the "do's" and "don'ts" of *Teasing* and *Being Selfish*, I'll pay just $5.48 per book, plus shipping and handling on the entire shipment, and become a member of the program.

Then, about four weeks later I'll receive two more books in the series. If I keep *Whining* and *Tattling*, I'll pay only $5.48 for each, plus shipping and handling.

About four weeks after that, I'll receive the remaining 24 books in a single shipment. This gives my child the complete series to read and enjoy, while I pay for only one book per month at $5.48 each, plus shipping and handling.

I may examine the books for seven days and return any I don't want at your expense. My FREE BOOK, *Disobeying*, FREE Sing-Along CDs, Parent's Guide and "Reading Together is Fun" Guide are mine to keep even if I purchase nothing.

Print Child's Full Name: _____   Birthdate: _____ ☐ Boy ☐ Girl

Month/Day/Year

Print Your Full Name   ☐ Mr. ☐ Mrs. ☐ Ms. _____

Address _____   Apt. _____

City _____   State _____   Zip _____

Telephone (_____) _____

E-mail (to confirm your order) _____

Have you bought anything by mail in the last: ☐ 6 months ☐ Year ☐ Never   Do you own a computer? ☐ Yes ☐ No

Sales tax where applicable. Late charges apply to overdue payments. All orders subject to approval. Out-of-stock titles may be replaced by alternate selections.

DETACH HERE AND MAIL TODAY!

Art © 1988 Living Skills Press

TM & © Scholastic Inc.

Mail today ...
and good behavior
will be on its way!

If card is missing, write to:
Help Me Be Good
c/o Scholastic
P.O. Box 6038
Jefferson City, MO 65102-6038

Help Me Be Good!

BUSINESS REPLY MAIL
FIRST-CLASS MAIL   PERMIT NO. 48   JEFFERSON CITY, MO

POSTAGE WILL BE PAID BY ADDRESSEE

SCHOLASTIC
PO BOX 6113
JEFFERSON CITY MO 65102-9669

Well-behaved kids start with these FREE GIFTS!

FREE CDs!

FREE Parents Guide

FREE Reading Guide

FREE TRIAL!

FREE BOOK!

card is missing,
ite to:
Help Me Be Good
c/o Scholastic
P.O. Box 6038
Jefferson City, MO
65102-6038

Instead of saying "no-no"... say "YES" to good behavior!

CODE: 964803WVA-3

☐ **YES!** Please send my FREE BOOK, *Disobeying*, FREE BONUS GIFTS, the Sing-Along CDs, Parent's Guide, and "Reading Together is Fun" Guide, plus two more Help Me Be Good books, *Being Selfish* and *Teasing*, for my seven-day free preview.

If not delighted with my trial books, I'll return them at your expense and owe nothing. On the other hand, if they help my child understand the "do's" and "don'ts" of *Teasing* and *Being Selfish*, I'll pay just $5.48 per book, plus shipping and handling on the entire shipment, and become a member of the program.

Then, about four weeks later I'll receive two more books in the series. If I keep *Whining* and *Tattling*, I'll pay only $5.48 for each, plus shipping and handling.

About four weeks after that, I'll receive the remaining 24 books in a single shipment. This gives my child the complete series to read and enjoy, while I pay for only one book per month at $5.48 each, plus shipping and handling.

I may examine the books for seven days and return any I don't want at your expense. My FREE BOOK, *Disobeying*, FREE Sing-Along CDs, Parent's Guide and "Reading Together is Fun" Guide are mine to keep even if I purchase nothing.

Print Child's Full Name: _____   Birthdate: _____   ☐ Boy ☐ Girl

Month/Day/Year

Print Your Full Name   ☐ Mr. ☐ Mrs. ☐ Ms. _____

Address _____   Apt. _____

City _____   State _____   Zip _____

Telephone (_____) _____

E-mail (to confirm your order) _____

Have you bought anything by mail in the last: ☐ 6 months ☐ Year ☐ Never   Do you own a computer? ☐ Yes ☐ No

Sales tax where applicable. Late charges apply to overdue payments. All orders subject to approval. Out-of-stock titles may be replaced by alternate selections.

DETACH HERE AND MAIL TODAY!   Art © 1988 Living Skills Press   TM & © Scholastic Inc.

Mail today ...
and good behavior
will be on its way!

If card is missing, write to:
Help Me Be Good
c/o Scholastic
P.O. Box 6038
Jefferson City, MO 65102-6038

Mail today ...
and good behavior
will be on its way!

If card is missing, write to:
Help Me Be Good
c/o Scholastic
P.O. Box 6038
Jefferson City, MO 65102-6038

Well-behaved kids start with these FREE GIFTS!

FREE CDs!
FREE Parents Guide
FREE Reading Guide
FREE BOOK!
FREE TRIAL!

...rd is missing,
...e to:
...lp Me Be Good
...o Scholastic
...D. Box 6038
...fferson City, MO
...102-6038

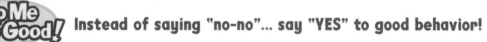

Instead of saying "no-no"... say "YES" to good behavior!

CODE: 964803WVA-3

☐ **YES!** Please send my FREE BOOK, *Disobeying*, FREE BONUS GIFTS, the Sing-Along CDs, Parent's Guide, and "Reading Together is Fun" Guide, plus two more Help Me Be Good books, *Being Selfish* and *Teasing*, for my seven-day free preview.

If not delighted with my trial books, I'll return them at your expense and owe nothing. On the other hand, if they help my child understand the "do's" and "don'ts" of *Teasing* and *Being Selfish*, I'll pay just $5.48 per book, plus shipping and handling on the entire shipment, and become a member of the program.

Then, about four weeks later I'll receive two more books in the series. If I keep *Whining* and *Tattling*, I'll pay only $5.48 for each, plus shipping and handling. About four weeks after that, I'll receive the remaining 24 books in a single shipment. This gives my child the complete series to read and enjoy, while I pay for only one book per month at $5.48 each, plus shipping and handling.

I may examine the books for seven days and return any I don't want at your expense. My FREE BOOK, *Disobeying*, FREE Sing-Along CDs, Parent's Guide and "Reading Together is Fun" Guide are mine to keep even if I purchase nothing.

Print Child's Full Name: _____   Birthdate: _____ ☐ Boy ☐ Girl

Month/Day/Year

Print Your Full Name ☐ Mr. ☐ Mrs. ☐ Ms. _____

Address _____   Apt. _____

City_____   State _____   Zip _____

Telephone (_____) _____

E-mail (to confirm your order) _____

Have you bought anything by mail in the last: ☐ 6 months ☐ Year ☐ Never   Do you own a computer? ☐ Yes ☐ No

Sales tax where applicable. Late charges apply to overdue payments. All orders subject to approval. Out-of-stock titles may be replaced by alternate selections.

DETACH HERE AND MAIL TODAY!

TM & © Scholastic Inc.   Art © 1988 Living Skills Press

Mail today ★★★
and good behavior
will be on its way!

If card is missing, write to:
Help Me Be Good
c/o Scholastic
P.O. Box 6038
Jefferson City, MO 65102-6038

Well-behaved kids start with these FREE GIFTS!

FREE CDs!

FREE Parents Guide

FREE Reading Guide

FREE TRIAL!

FREE BOOK!

...rd is missing,
...e to:
...lp Me Be Good
... Scholastic
... Box 6038
...fferson City, MO
...102-6038

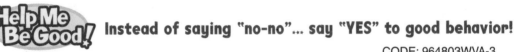

Instead of saying "no-no"... say "YES" to good behavior!

CODE: 964803WVA-3

☐ **YES!** Please send my FREE BOOK, *Disobeying*, FREE BONUS GIFTS, the Sing-Along CDs, Parent's Guide, and "Reading Together is Fun" Guide, plus two more Help Me Be Good books, *Being Selfish* and *Teasing*, for my seven-day free preview.

If not delighted with my trial books, I'll return them at your expense and owe nothing. On the other hand, if they help my child understand the "do's" and "don'ts" of *Teasing* and *Being Selfish*, I'll pay just $5.48 per book, plus shipping and handling on the entire shipment, and become a member of the program.

Then, about four weeks later I'll receive two more books in the series. If I keep *Whining* and *Tattling*, I'll pay only $5.48 for each, plus shipping and handling.

About four weeks after that, I'll receive the remaining 24 books in a single shipment. This gives my child the complete series to read and enjoy, while I pay for only one book per month at $5.48 each, plus shipping and handling.

I may examine the books for seven days and return any I don't want at your expense. My FREE BOOK, *Disobeying*, FREE Sing-Along CDs, Parent's Guide and "Reading Together is Fun" Guide are mine to keep even if I purchase nothing.

Print Child's Full Name: _____ Birthdate: _____ ☐ Boy ☐ Girl

Month/Day/Year

Print Your Full Name ☐ Mr. ☐ Mrs. ☐ Ms. _____

Address _____ Apt. _____

City_____ State _____ Zip _____

Telephone (_____) _____

E-mail (to confirm your order) _____

Have you bought anything by mail in the last: ☐ 6 months ☐ Year ☐ Never   Do you own a computer? ☐ Yes ☐ No

Sales tax where applicable. Late charges apply to overdue payments. All orders subject to approval. Out-of-stock titles may be replaced by alternate selections.

DETACH HERE AND MAIL TODAY!

TM & © Scholastic Inc.   Art © 1988 Living Skills Press

Mail today ...

and good behavior will be on its way!

If card is missing, write to:
Help Me Be Good
c/o Scholastic
P.O. Box 6038
Jefferson City, MO 65102-6038

Help Me Be Good!

Well-behaved kids start with these FREE GIFTS!

FREE CDs!
FREE Parents Guide
FREE Reading Guide
FREE BOOK!
FREE TRIAL!

card is missing,
ite to:
Help Me Be Good
c/o Scholastic
P.O. Box 6038
Jefferson City, MO
65102-6038

Instead of saying "no-no"... say "YES" to good behavior!

CODE: 964803WVA-3

☐ **YES!** Please send my FREE BOOK, *Disobeying*, FREE BONUS GIFTS, the Sing-Along CDs, Parent's Guide, and "Reading Together is Fun" Guide, plus two more Help Me Be Good books, *Being Selfish* and *Teasing*, for my seven-day free preview.

If not delighted with my trial books, I'll return them at your expense and owe nothing. On the other hand, if they help my child understand the "do's" and "don'ts" of *Teasing* and *Being Selfish*, I'll just pay $5.48 per book, plus shipping and handling on the entire shipment, and become a member of the program.

Then, about four weeks later I'll receive two more books in the series. If I keep *Whining* and *Tattling*, I'll pay only $5.48 for each, plus shipping and handling.

About four weeks after that, I'll receive the remaining 24 books in a single shipment. This gives my child the complete series to read and enjoy, while I pay for only one book per month at $5.48 each, plus shipping and handling.

I may examine the books for seven days and return any I don't want at your expense. My FREE BOOK, *Disobeying*, FREE Sing-Along CDs, Parent's Guide and "Reading Together is Fun" Guide are mine to keep even if I purchase nothing.

Print Child's Full Name: _____ Birthdate: _____ ☐ Boy ☐ Girl

Month/Day/Year

Print Your Full Name ☐ Mr. ☐ Mrs. ☐ Ms. _____

Address _____ Apt. _____

City_____ State _____ Zip _____

Telephone (_____) _____

E-mail (to confirm your order) _____

Have you bought anything by mail in the last: ☐ 6 months ☐ Year ☐ Never   Do you own a computer? ☐ Yes ☐ No

Sales tax where applicable. Late charges apply to overdue payments. All orders subject to approval. Out-of-stock titles may be replaced by alternate selections.

DETACH HERE AND MAIL TODAY!

Art © 1988 Living Skills Press

TM & © Scholastic Inc.

Mail today ...
and good behavior
will be on its way!

If card is missing, write to:
Help Me Be Good
c/o Scholastic
P.O. Box 6038
Jefferson City, MO 65102-6038

Mail today ...
and good behavior
will be on its way!

If card is missing, write to:
Help Me Be Good
c/o Scholastic
P.O. Box 6038
Jefferson City, MO 65102-6038

Mail today ...
and good behavior
will be on its way!

If card is missing, write to:
Help Me Be Good
c/o Scholastic
P.O. Box 6038
Jefferson City, MO 65102-6038

■ SCHOLASTIC

P.O. BOX 6038, JEFFERSON CITY, MO 65102-6038
www.HomeClubs.Scholastic.com

Dear Parent,

We want to send you *Help Me Be Good* storybooks to encourage your child's good behavior … and love of reading.

As the most trusted name in learning today, we know just what that takes! Scholastic's books have been used by thousands of teachers across the country to teach millions of children to read. We're the #1 resource for parents like you for the widest variety of innovative products that help their children learn at home.

Parents turn to us to find just the right products for their children's specific needs and interests. From programs to enrich their children's skills … sensible solutions to pressing concerns … homework help, research projects, reading tips and more.

After all, we're parents, too! And, speaking as a mom, these *Help Me Be Good* storybooks have made a welcomed difference in our family. My kids love the funny cartoon-style stories. I love the way that each book shares a positive lesson about "growing up" – helping my kids understand and why it's so important to always tell the truth, obey your parents, to share with others, and other good behaviors. These are books that are sure to be read again and again.

So, enjoy this book with your child right now. Then fill out and mail one of the order cards at left and watch your child start learning … and loving every minute of it!

Sincerely,

Mary-Alice Moore

Mary-Alice Moore
Editorial Director and mother of three

(and mother of three!)

NOTE: If all of the cards are missing, please write to:
Help Me Be Good, c/o Scholastic,
P.O. Box 6038, Jefferson City, MO 65102-6038

Help Me
Be Good!

A NOTE TO PARENTS ABOUT DISOBEYING

"Because I told you so!" is, in most cases, an insufficient motivation for children to obey their parents. Like adults, children want and need to know the rationale behind requests they are expected to fulfill.

The purpose of this book is to help children understand the basis for parental authority. In addition, it explains the importance of being obedient and tells children how to rectify situations in which they have disobeyed.

Reading and discussing this book with your child will motivate him or her to choose obedience over disobedience. It should also decrease your need to be a disciplinarian and will give you more time to be the loving, supportive parent you want to be.

Most disobedience can be avoided by making sure children know exactly what is expected of them. Disobedience can also be avoided by involving children in the formulation of the rules and regulations for which they are responsible. Children, like adults, are more willing to comply with self-imposed guidelines rather than ones that are externally imposed. Therefore, any time invested in making your child's good behavior a team effort will result in less time spent on discipline and punishment.

This book belongs to:

_____

Published by Scholastic Inc.
90 Old Sherman Turnpike, Danbury, CT 06816.

SCHOLASTIC and associated logos are trademarks and/or
registered trademarks of Scholastic Inc.

ISBN 0-7172-8593-6

First Scholastic Printing, September 2005

A Book About
Disobeying

by **Joy Berry**

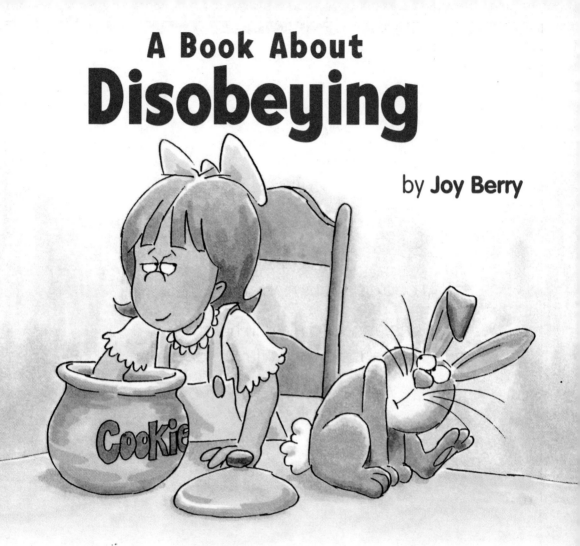

SCHOLASTIC INC.

New York   Toronto   London   Auckland   Sydney
Mexico City   New Delhi   Hong Kong   Buenos Aires

This book is about Annie.

Reading about Annie can help you
understand and deal with **disobeying.**

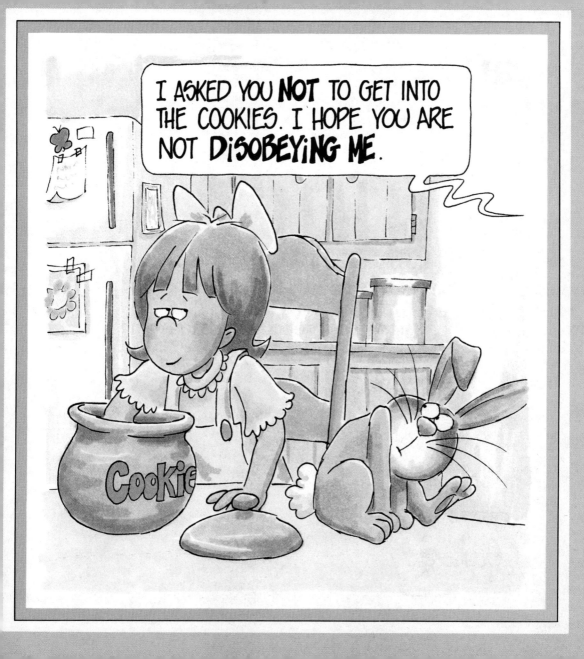

You are disobeying when you do not do what you have been told to do.

Your parents have good reasons for telling you what to do. This is why you should not disobey them.

Your parents tell you what to do because they do not want you to hurt yourself or others.

Your parents tell you what to do because they do not want you to damage or destroy things.

Your parents tell you what to do because they want you to be liked by other people.

Your parents tell you what to do because they want you to be fair.

Sometimes you might wonder why parents get to tell their children what to do.

Parents tell their children what to do because they have lived longer and have learned more than children.

Thus, parents usually know what is best for their children.

Parents tell their children what to do because they are responsible for their children.

Parents have to take care of the damage when their children hurt themselves or others.

Sometimes parents need to punish their children for disobeying.

The purpose of a punishment is to make children feel bad about disobeying so they will not disobey again.

You can avoid being punished if you do
these things:

- Talk to your parents.
- Find out what they want you to do. Then
  do it.

Sometimes you might not agree with your parents. Tell them how you feel.

They might change their minds. If they do not change their minds, drop the subject.

Nagging and throwing tantrums will only frustrate you and make your parents angry.

Tell the truth if you disobey.

Admit that you disobeyed.

Say that you are sorry and mean it.

Accept your punishment if you disobey.

Do not be angry at your parents when they punish you. Remember, it was you who disobeyed, not them.

Try not to disobey again.

When you obey, you please your parents, and you are doing what is best for you.